the B*g G**o

in

THE BIG
BAD WOLF

OK.
I know this seems bad . . .

BAD?!
Mr. Wolf has turned into an
EVIL, UNSTOPPABLE MONSTER the size of a
FOOTBALL STADIUM!
This isn't just bad, *chica*!
It's . . .

But it is!

Wolf made **EVERYTHING SEEM POSSIBLE.**

Without him, we're just **A BUNCH OF CROOKS.**

And without him leading the way · · ·

· · · you feel lost.

I get it. But · · ·

No buts!

There's *nothing* you can say to make this better, *señorita.*

The **ALIENS** have taken over the world,

Wolf is **TOO BIG** and **TOO LOÇO** to be stopped,

and **ALL HOPE IS LOST!**

Full respect to you and the League of Heroes, but *no one in the world could make this seem OK!*

Someone could.

Wolf could.

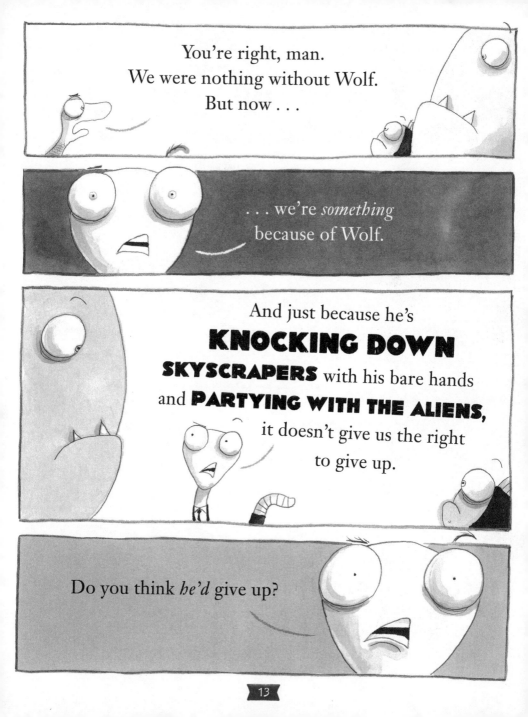

You're right, man.
We were nothing without Wolf.
But now . . .

. . . we're *something*
because of Wolf.

And just because he's
**KNOCKING DOWN
SKYSCRAPERS** with his bare hands
and **PARTYING WITH THE ALIENS,**
it doesn't give us the right
to give up.

Do you think *he'd* give up?

Or do you think he'd open his **BIG, STUPID MOUTH** and say something idiotic like . . .

"Hey, Piranha! You've got **SUPER SPEED!** That's a big deal, *hermano!*"

Or . . . "Shark! You're a **SHAPE-SHIFTER,** dude! Disguise yourself as something that will get us out of this mess!"

Or . . . "Legs! What do we do here? You're the smartest **NON-VELOCIRAPTOR** I know!"

"They are the **BEST OF THE BEST!**"

Yes, we are.

And so are we!

Uh, no.
No, that's . . .
No.

So, everyone put in your earbuds and clip on your microphones . . .

This is how it's going down:

HALF OF US
need to keep going with

OPERATION TARANTULA.

We need to get our eight-legged buddy and Agent Shortfuse onto that **MOTHER SHIP.**

Legs has to **TAKE CONTROL** of that thing. It's the only way we'll stop those aliens.

Half of us?!
But what do the
OTHER HALF do?

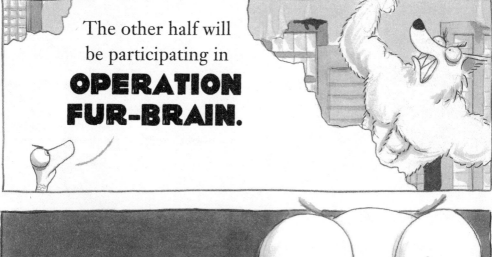

The other half will
be participating in
**OPERATION
FUR-BRAIN.**

It's time to get
our big, hairy
buddy back.

· CHAPTER 2 ·

GOOD-BYE, FOR NOW

That *hombre* is *big*!
You'll never get any
closer than this.
What's your **PLAN**, *chico*?

That's not your problem.
Your problem is getting
THOSE TWO onto that
MOTHER SHIP.

Good luck, guys.

Your plan is to watch him **THROW BUSES?** What? Are you hoping he'll just get sore arms and take a power nap?

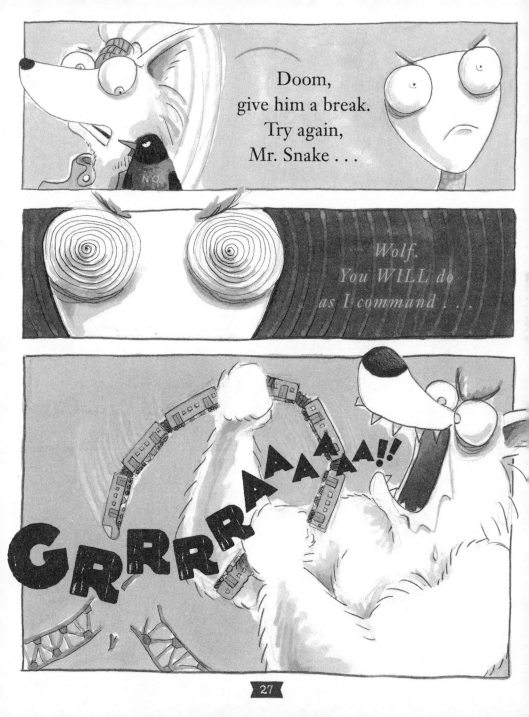

· CHAPTER 3 ·
NEW WINGS

OK, *listen up!*
That alien trash **BLEW UP MY JET,**
so we have to get ourselves one of those
ZIPPY LITTLE SPACESHIPS.
THAT'S how we get to the big one.

Legs?
YOU are going to teach me
how to fly one of those things
in the **TWO MINUTES**
it takes to get us up there . . .

THEN you and
Shortfuse will get in this
PROJECTILE . . .

so I can fire you both **ONTO THAT MOTHER SHIP.** Then I'll fly the rest of us back here. Any questions?

Well, yes . . . I . . .

Good! Then let's **MOVE OUT!**

• CHAPTER 4 •
IN ONE EAR...

MR. WOLF!

That sounds a little formal, doesn't it? *Agent Fox.* It's funny . . . I just realized . . .

I've never told you my real name, have I?

Well, it's high time I did. Allow me to introduce myself, Mr. Wolf. My name is . . .

I am SO out of here.

Thanks for the ride.

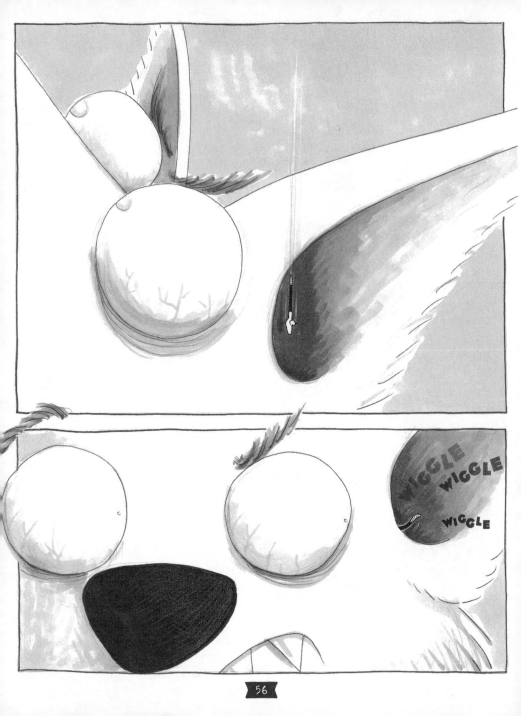

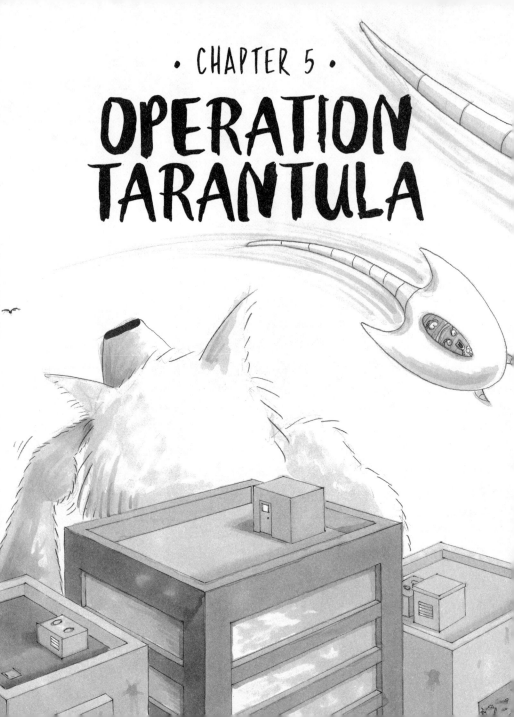

· CHAPTER 5 ·
OPERATION TARANTULA

ZAP! ZAP!

AAR GRR GGHHH!!!

They're on to us!
We'll never make it!

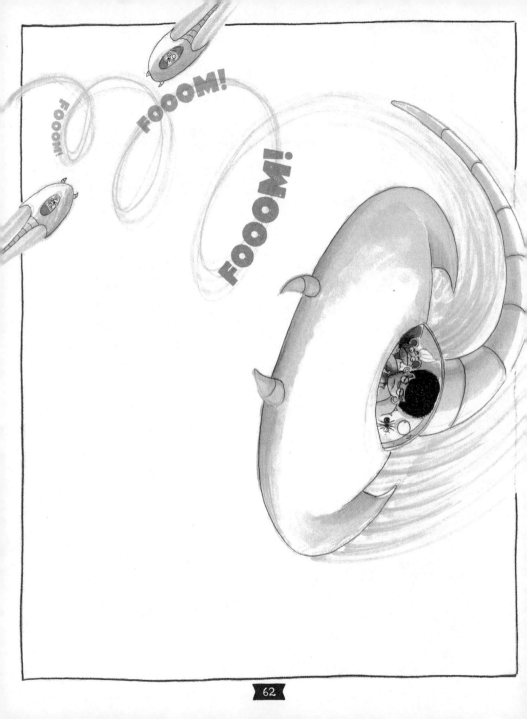

Now GET INTO YOUR CONTAINER!
I'm going to launch you onto
the mother ship from the
GARBAGE CHUTE.

But won't they see us launch?
We'll be sitting ducks . . .

They won't even notice *your* tiny butts because they'll be too **DUMBFOUNDED** by Mr. Shark. Isn't that right, big guy?

Are you asking me to **CREATE A DISTRACTION** using my uncanny ability to **DISGUISE MYSELF?**

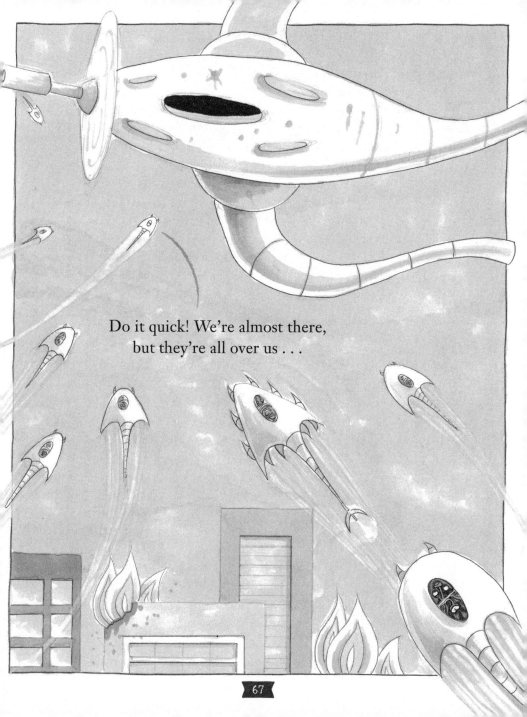

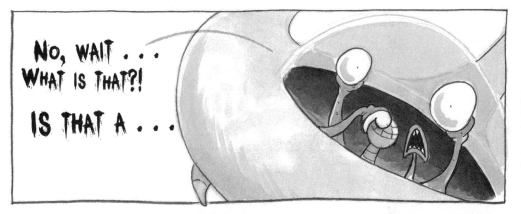

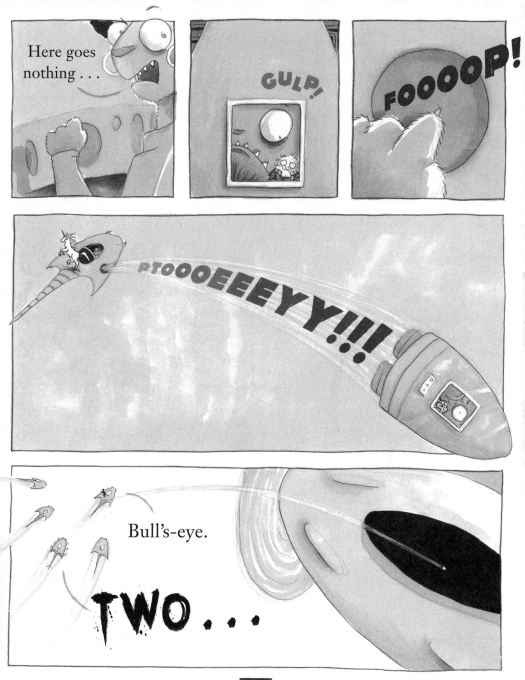

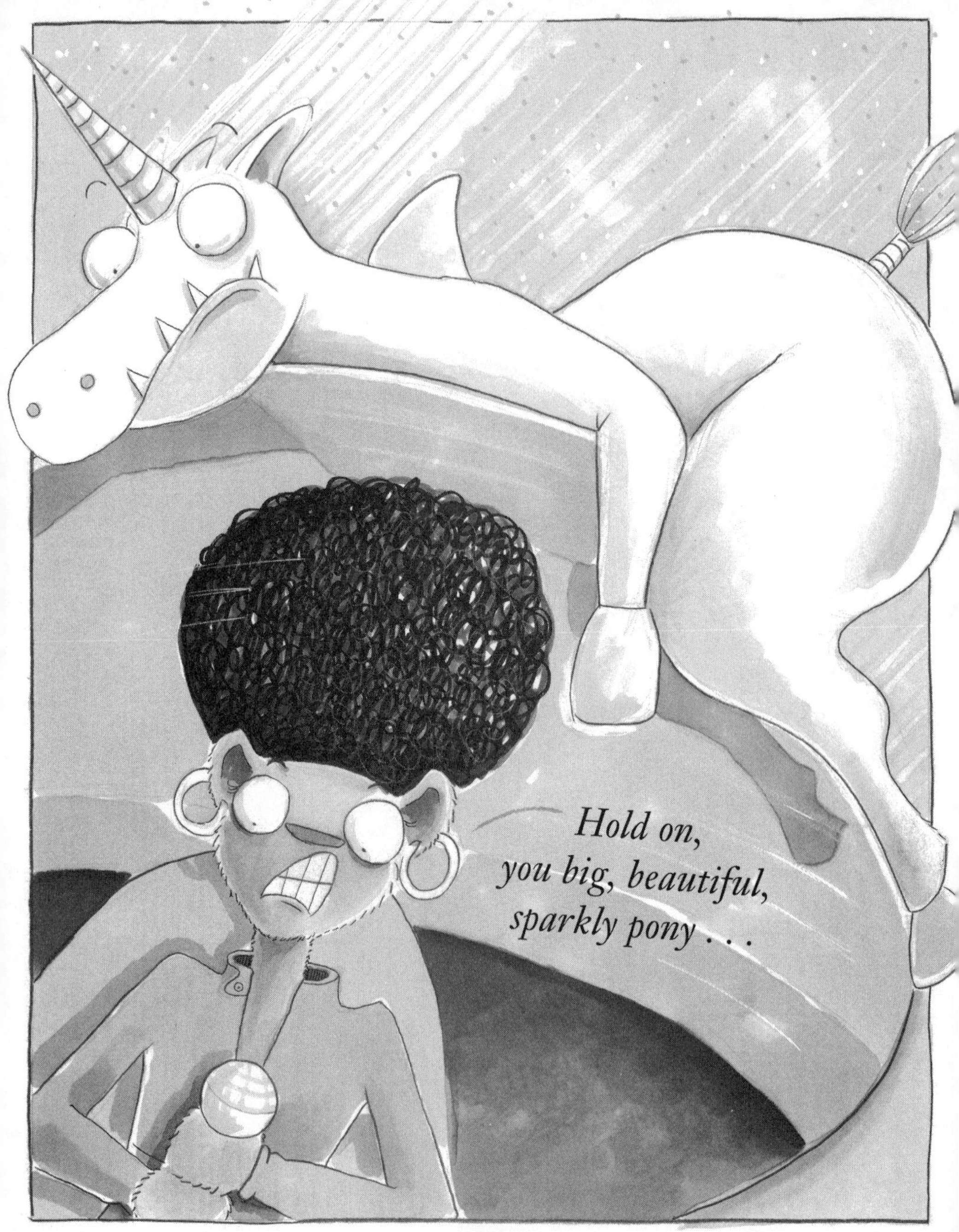
Hold on,
you big, beautiful,
sparkly pony . . .

WE'RE
GOING DOWN!

CHAPTER 6 ·
THE WOLF WHISPERER

Oh man.
This is disgusting.

You WILL stop this.
You WILL calm down.
You WILL return to normal.

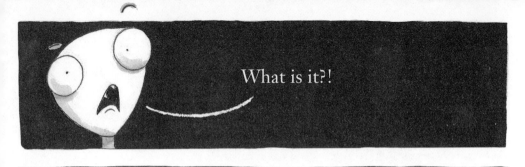

What is it?!

Well. I just upgraded to some high-quality **HEADPHONES** because those little **EARBUDS** you're all wearing won't be comfortably accommodated by my **PRIMORDIAL EAR HOLES.**

It's been quite a trial.

But fear not, these new ones

are really quite excellent . . .

HOW IS THIS RELEVANT?!

Well, that's the thing. These headphones are of such a high standard that they seem to have picked up on **ANOTHER SIGNAL** coming from Mr. Wolf's enormous head.

What kind of signal . . . ?

Well. Unless I'm *very* much mistaken, I suspect there's **SOMEONE ELSE** lurking about in his **OTHER EAR.**

YEP! HI, EVERYBODY!
I'VE BEEN WHISPERING SWEET NOTHINGS TO THIS FLEABAG ALL MORNING, AND HE'S PROVED TO BE TREMENDOUSLY USEFUL.
BUT THIS IS MY PARTY, MR. SNAKE—I'M AFRAID I'LL HAVE TO ASK YOU TO KEEP IT DOWN.

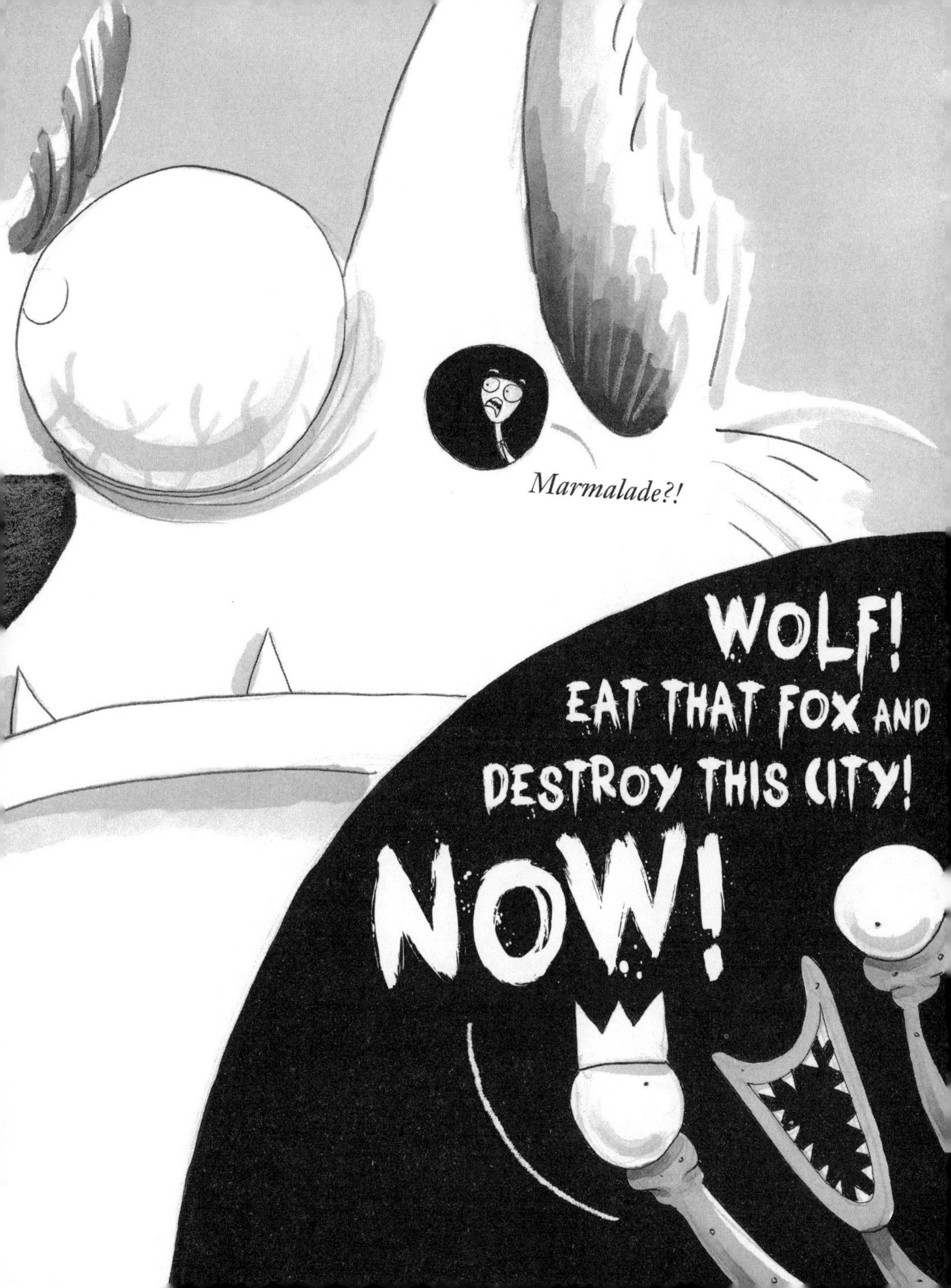
Marmalade?!
WOLF! EAT THAT FOX AND DESTROY THIS CITY!
NOW!

• CHAPTER 7 •

WHO NEEDS SUPERPOWERS?

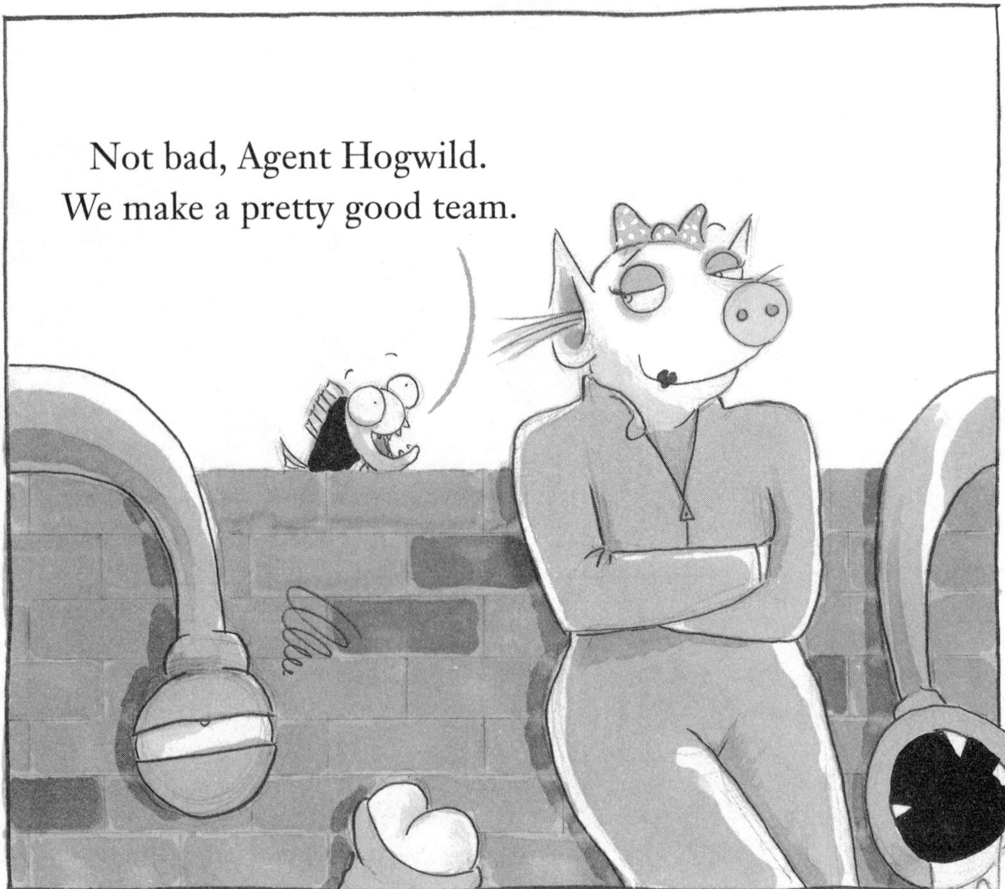

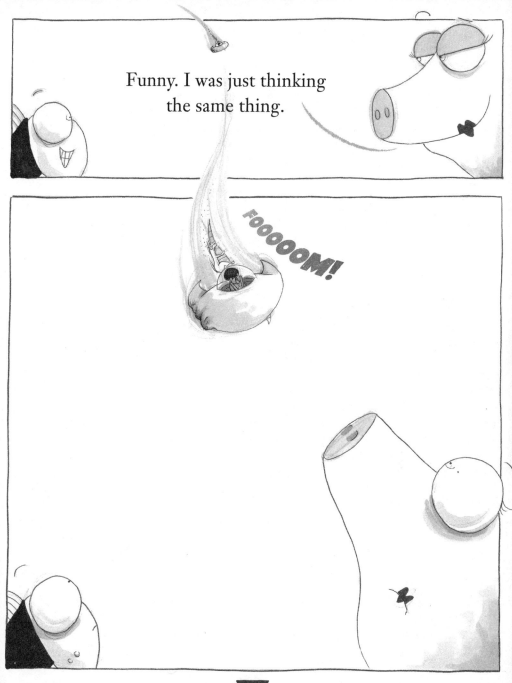

Was that a . . . *UNICORN*?!

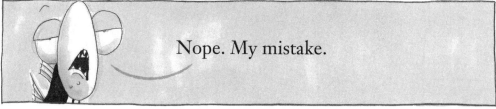

Nope. My mistake.

HELP!

Welcome back, guys,
but we'd better move.

FOX IS IN TROUBLE . . .

SMASH!

GRRRAAAHH!!

WOLF!
YOU WILL STOP THIS!
YOU WILL CALM DOWN!
YOU WILL RETURN TO NORMAL!

WOLF!
SMASH!

Hey, Wolf?

Yeah I'm talking to *you*, Butt Brain.

Look, man, enough's enough. I'm waist-deep in earwax here,

and my patience has **RUN OUT.**

What you're doing is **BAD.** Do you hear me?

You're behaving like a **BAD GUY.**

And at this point, that is *very* disappointing, dude.

So for our sake, and for the sake of

everything you've worked for . . .

I need you to **CUT IT OUT.**

• CHAPTER 8 •
THE FALL

HOOOOWWWL!!

Mr. Wolf?

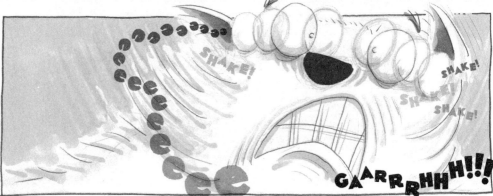

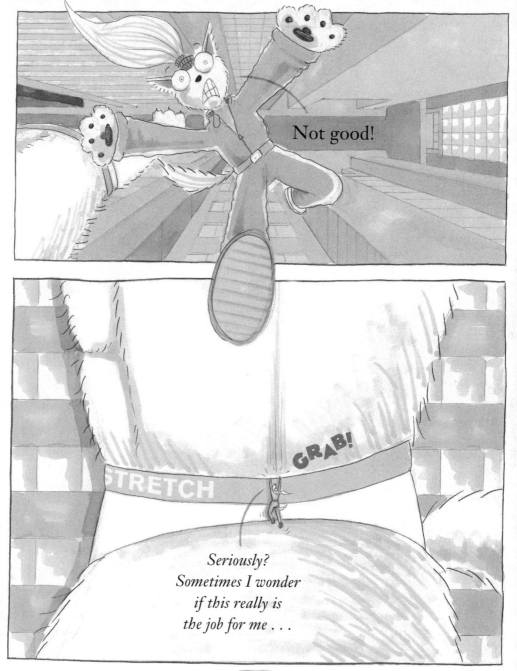

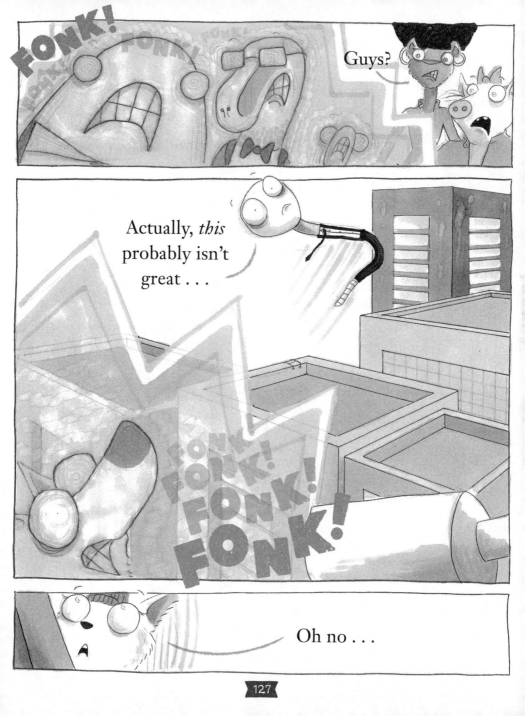

FONK!
FONK!
FONK!
FONK!
FONK!
FONK!
FONK!
FONK!
FONK!
FONK!

Mr. Wolf!
You're shrinking!

· CHAPTER 9 ·
THE DARKEST HOUR

That's it, Butt Hands!
Let's blast up there and
take him down!

Whaaa . . . wait a minute!
My **SUPER SPEED** . . .
it's . . .

Gone. So is my power.
I CAN'T CHANGE.
He must have taken it all
away with that weird blast.

And why's he wearing a **CROWN**
all of a sudden?

GREAT QUESTION!
YOU MUST BE BUSTING
TO ASK ME SO MANY THINGS.

... OH YES,
OF COURSE ...

YOUR LITTLE BUDDY
MR. SNAKE IS GONE
FOREVER!